This journal contains
the daily thoughts of

_____

_____

Date

"I know the plans I have for
you," declares the Lord,
"plans to prosper you and not
to harm you, plans to give
you hope and a future."
Jeremiah 29:11